VILLAINS
GUIDE

Written by Jacqueline Rayner

THE ADVENTURES OF MERLIN – THE VILLAINS GUIDE

A BANTAM BOOK 978 0 553 82231 1

First published in Great Britain by Bantam,
an imprint of Random House Children's Books
A Random House Group Company

This edition published 2010

1 3 5 7 9 10 8 6 4 2

Bantam Books are published by Random House Children's Books,
61–63 Uxbridge Road, London W5 5SA

www.**rbooks**.co.uk
www.**kids**at**randomhouse**.co.uk

Addresses for companies within The Random House Group Limited can be found at:
www.**randomhouse**.co.uk/offices.htm

THE RANDOM HOUSE GROUP Limited Reg. No. 954009

A CIP catalogue record for this book is available from the British Library

Printed in China

THE
VILLAINS
GUIDE

Written by Jacqueline Rayner

CONTENTS

WHAT IS A VILLAIN?

VILLAIN (male and female): Someone of dubious moral standing who performs evil acts and deeds that hurt and harm those around him. A villain thinks only of himself and acts solely for his own gain.

THE NUMBER'S UP
How many times is the word VILLAIN hidden
in the wordsearch below?

```
V I L L A I N X C V B N Y N I A L L I V
Q I D C V B N M K J G H Y U J I K S D T
S X L A V H N M L P A J T G F D S C R V
T B P L Q X W C V B N H G F D R T B N Y
Z X P L A A X F G I P L V I L L A I N R
R C B H Y I A Q G Y H B I Y G F R M A X
R C V B H T N W D C U I L I L L A W I Q
R F C V V I L L A I N V L C B N M H L J
Q S D C V B N M P Y U H A R F V G H L S
X V B Y H N J I O P E R I Q S C B J I R
Q C V P O G V I L L A I N Q P L T Y V S
U G E T Y I F V V B J M G F G V B N J U
H F S D L F G H I S D C V G H Y G B S U
F G S L E R V T L A S D C N D F V B N J
T G A S D C I W L W D D G B I S D F G V
W I W B J M L C A C R B N N I A L L I V
N S D G N K L I I H J K L P I G L F E S
F H C M I A T N N K T H K T F H L F D
H J V Y G H I V I L L A I N G J K T I D
V I L L A I N R G H J R K O I D D F G V
```

The word VILLAIN appears _____ times.

A DARK SHADOW

Merlin, Arthur and their friends have met some pretty nasty villains. Can you work out who some of the most fearsome have been by looking at their silhouettes below? There are clues to help you.

1 This murderous villain held Merlin's home town under siege.

2 Using the Mage Stone, this villain tried to turn base metal into gold.

3 The spirit of this long dead sorcerer possessed a servant to try and bring down Camelot.

4 The half-sister of Morgana, she used her sibling to infiltrate Camelot.

5 She conjured an Afanc to pollute Camelot's water supply.

MARY COLLINS

A MOTHER'S LOVE

When King Uther executed Thomas Collins for using magic, Thomas' mother Mary swore vengeance. Mary demonstrated her own powers when she escaped the execution by magical means; a clear act of defiance before the king.

VILLAINY RATING	
Evil intent	★★★
Magical power	★★★★
Desire for revenge	★★★★★
Sneakiness	★★★★
Comeuppance	★★★★★

VILLAINOUS DEEDS

Mary decided to kill Uther's son, as he had killed hers. Using a magic poppet, she ruthlessly killed the famed singer Lady Helen of Mora, who was due to perform for Uther. During her stay in Camelot she showed no compunction when she drained the life of a servant girl who had seen her true appearance.

'Lady Helen' performed for King Uther and his court – but her singing was enchanted. As Mary Collins sang, sleep and decay spread through the palace.

The only person who resisted the spell was Merlin, because he had realized 'Helen' was not who she seemed. Mary drew a knife to murder the helpless Prince Arthur, but Merlin brought a candelabrum down on her head.

FAILED PLANS

Mary died knowing she had not succeeded in gaining her revenge. What she didn't realize was that her actions actually benefited Uther; as thanks for saving the prince, Merlin was made Arthur's servant, and he would go on to save Uther and Arthur's lives on many occasions.

VILLAINOUS WORDS

'There is only one evil in this land and it is not magic – it is you!'
Mary to Uther (*The Dragon's Call*)

'You took my son and I promise you – before these celebrations are over, you will share my tears! An eye for an eye, a tooth for a tooth, a son for a son!'
Mary to Uther (*The Dragon's Call*)

DID YOU KNOW?
Mary used a magical pendant to help her cast spells.

VALIANT

A DARK KNIGHT

Valiant was a villain through
and through. He was not
a wronged victim seeking
revenge; he cared only for
himself and he did not
hesitate to kill in order
to achieve his purpose
– to win the Camelot
tournament. Valiant was
determined that glory,
fame, and the prize
of one thousand gold
pieces would all be his
– no matter what.

VILLAINOUS DEEDS

Though not magic himself, Valiant obtained a magical shield with a crest of three snakes, each of which would come to life when ordered – and their bites were deadly! Before setting off for Camelot, Valiant calmly murdered the man who crafted the weapon.

VILLAINOUS WORDS

'Valiant's going to fight Arthur in the final. He'll use the shield to kill him!'

Merlin *(Valiant)*

'You should stay in Camelot after the tournament. I could do with more knights like you.'

Uther to Valiant *(Valiant)*

DID YOU KNOW?

Knight Valiant came from the Western Isles.

VILLAINOUS DEEDS

It soon became clear that if Valiant couldn't beat an opponent then he used his enchanted shield to claim victory. Valiant fooled everyone except Merlin. Even Uther thought Valiant was perfect; urging Arthur to be more like him.

FAILED PLANS

Valiant faced Arthur in the final but Merlin exposed the villainous knight. In a cowardly move, Valiant ordered the snakes to kill the unarmed prince. Luckily, Morgana threw Arthur a sword and Valiant swiftly met his end.

NIMUEH

SEASON OF THE WITCH

Nimueh was a priestess of the old religion, a religion that has existed since the beginning of the world. It serves the earth itself and is concerned only with maintaining order and the balance of nature, whatever the cost. Unfortunately for Merlin and Arthur, Nimueh's faith became corrupted by a desire for revenge against the person who tried to wipe out her kind – the king of Camelot, Uther Pendragon.

VILLAINY RATING	
Evil intent	★★★★★
Magical power	★★★★★
Desire for revenge	★★★★★
Sneakiness	★★★★★
Comeuppance	★★★★★

VILLAINOUS DEEDS

Uther and Nimueh were once friends, and the king asked her to provide him with a son through magical means. But when Nimueh granted his wish, the old religion took his wife, Ygraine – a life for a life in exchange – leaving Uther with a violent hatred of everything magical.

In revenge Nimueh conjured an Afanc to infect Camelot's water supply. She poisoned Arthur's goblet in an attempt to start a war between Camelot and Mercia, and she raised the Black Knight from the dead in an attempt to kill the king.

VILLAINOUS DEEDS

Even when directly serving the old religion, Nimueh showed no compassion. She agreed to save Arthur's life but ignored Merlin's request to take his own life in exchange. Instead, she took the life of his mother. Then, when Gaius came to offer his own life for Merlin's, Nimueh taunted the old physician and seemed to enjoy bringing about his death.

FAILED PLANS

These final actions were Nimueh's undoing. Grief-stricken, Merlin summoned all his power, calling down a bolt of lightning to destroy the sorceress. The balance of the world was restored and Gaius was returned to life.

VILLAINOUS WORDS

'I have watched so many people I love die at your hands, Uther Pendragon. Now it is your turn.'

Nimueh *(Excalibur)*

'You should not have killed my friend.'

Merlin to Nimueh *(Le Morte D'Arthur)*

DID YOU KNOW?

Nimueh looked like a beautiful young girl, but this was a disguise wrought by sorcery.

SOMETHING DIFFERENT

Mary Collins cast a deep enchantment over Camelot.
Look carefully at the scenes below – can you spot the ten
differences between the two pictures?

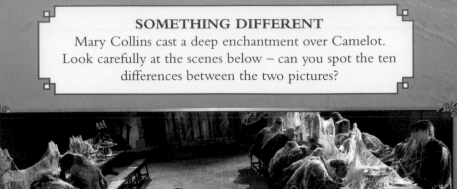

UNKNOWN ORIGIN

Knight Valiant travelled far to enter Camelot's tournament. Can you rearrange the letters below to discover where Valiant was really from?

SEE THE NEST SWIRL

Answer: T _ _ W _ _ T _ _ N I _ _ E S

EDWIN MUIRDEN

SORCEROR'S REVENGE

During the Great Purge, many sorcerers, including Edwin's parents, were burned at the stake. Edwin ran into the flames to try to rescue them and his face was badly burned. From then on he was consumed with a desire for revenge against the man who ordered his parents' deaths – Uther Pendragon.

VILLAINY RATING	
Evil intent	★★★
Magical power	★★★★
Desire for revenge	★★★★★
Sneakiness	★★★★
Comeuppance	★★★★★

VILLAINOUS DEEDS

Pain and grief twisted Edwin's mind until he thought nothing of hurting others in his quest for revenge. He used enchanted Elanthia Beetles to attack Morgana's brain, so he could 'cure' her and usurp Gaius' long-standing position as court physician.

Edwin hated Gaius for standing by while fellow magic-users were killed during the Great Purge, but that didn't stop Edwin himself from betraying other sorcerers. When Gaius discovered the newcomer's plot to murder Uther, Edwin threatened to expose Merlin as a warlock if Gaius didn't keep quiet.

FAILED PLANS

Edwin sent his Elanthia Beetles to attack Uther's brain. When Gaius tried to stop him, Edwin launched a murderous attack on the physician. Merlin intervened and Edwin turned on him. In the battle that followed, the axe that Edwin sent magically spinning towards the young warlock ended up in his own head . . .

VILLAINOUS WORDS

'Within hours the beetle will eat into your brain and you will suffer as they suffered. And I long to hear you scream as they screamed the night you gave the order for the fires to be lit.'

Edwin to Uther (*A Remedy to Cure All Ills*)

DID YOU KNOW?

Edwin adopted his mother's maiden name to disguise his true identity.

Aulfric Tirmawr

The Sacred Sidhe

Aulfric and Sophia were Sidhe: immortal faerie creatures from the magical world of Avalon. They were barred from Avalon and condemned to live as humans because Aulfric killed another Sidhe. He knew he could never make amends but hoped to secure Sophia's return to Avalon by presenting the Sidhe with the soul of a mortal prince – the soul of Arthur Pendragon.

VILLAINY RATING	
Evil intent	★★★
Magical power	★★★★
Desire for revenge	
Sneakiness	★★★
Comeuppance	★★★★★

24

VILLAINOUS DEEDS

When Arthur saw Aulfric and his daughter being attacked by bandits, he assumed they were in danger and stepped in to help. Arthur had no idea that the attack had been arranged by Aulfric in order to gain an introduction to the prince. Aulfric later killed the only remaining bandit with a deadly blast from his magic staff so that Arthur would never discover the truth.

FAILED PLANS

When Merlin did everything he could to protect Arthur, Aulfric tried to kill the young warlock. Luckily, Merlin's powers enabled him to survive. He tracked down the Sidhe before the sacrifice was complete and killed Aulfric with an energy bolt from Sophia's staff.

VILLAINOUS WORDS

'Your punishment for killing another Sidhe is a mortal body and a mortal life. You will never be able to return to Avalon.'

Sidhe Elder to Aulfric *(The Gates of Avalon)*

'The Sidhe are a vicious people.'

Gaius *(The Gates of Avalon)*

DID YOU KNOW?

The runes on Aulfric's staff read 'To hold life and death in your hands' in the ancient script, Ogham.

SOPHIA TIRMAWR

THE EXILED FAERIE

Sophia would have been surprised to be thought a villain. As a Sidhe – albeit an exiled one – she considered herself naturally superior to humans. She saw the sacrifice of Arthur as a means to an end. To her, humans were lesser creatures; there to be used.

VILLAINOUS DEEDS

Sophia enticed Arthur with enchantments, making him believe he loved her. He fell so deeply under her spell that he agreed to elope, and left Camelot by her side like a helpless lamb to the slaughter . . .

VILLAINY RATING	
Evil intent	★★★
Magical power	★★★
Desire for revenge	
Sneakiness	★★★★
Comeuppance	★★★★★

To regain her immortality and re-enter the Sidhe world of Avalon, Sophia needed to sacrifice the life of a mortal prince to the Sidhe. Arthur was to be that sacrifice. The ceremony, however, was a dangerous one – the Sidhe Elders expected to be given a soul, and if they did not get Arthur's they would take Sophia's instead.

FAILED PLANS

Sophia was still in her mortal, human body when Merlin arrived and turned her own staff on her so he could rescue Arthur. Sophia died a mortal death and, as she exploded into dust, the Sidhe Elders claimed her soul.

VILLAINOUS WORDS

'For a moment I felt what it would be like to die a mortal death.'

Sophia *(The Gates of Avalon)*

'Once his heart is yours the gates of Avalon will open once again for us and we can regain our true form.'

Aulfric to Sophia *(The Gates of Avalon)*

'Sophia plans to sacrifice you to buy a life of immortality! If you go with her, you'll die!'

Merlin to Arthur *(The Gates of Avalon)*

DID YOU KNOW?

When Sophia performed magic her eyes glowed red.

BEETLE CHASE

Edwin used Elanthia Beetles to try and devour Uther's brain. Look carefully at the picture below — how many can you spot crawling around here?

Answer:

A DANGEROUS MIND

When Edwin comes to Camelot he only has one thing on his mind. Can you rearrange the letters below to work out what Edwin is thinking?

A V E E G E N C N

Answer: _ _ _ _ _ _ _ _ _

MIRROR, MIRROR

Sophia scrawled the details of her villainous plan onto her mirror. Using your own mirror, place it next to the page to decipher what she intends to do.

To save myself form a mortal death I must offer another mortal soul in sacrifice

Answer:

_____

_____

_____

_____

_____

Although Aulfric and Sophia look human, they are really from a magical race. Cross out all letters that appear twice below to reveal what they are.

S Y
W A T T J Y
B I D W
J H A B E

Answer: _ _ _ _ _

31

THE BLACK KNIGHT

VILLAINY RATING	
Evil intent	★★★
Magical power	★★★★★
Desire for revenge	★★★★★
Sneakiness	
Comeuppance	★★★★★

THE EVIL DEAD

The Black Knight came to Camelot determined to seek his revenge on Uther Pendragon. But there was one difference between him and Uther's other enemies – the Black Knight had already been killed by the king once before . . .

VILLAINOUS DEEDS

Sir Tristan de Bois, the brother of Uther's wife Ygraine, blamed Uther for Ygraine's death. Soon after she was buried, Tristan came to the gates of Camelot and challenged the king to single combat. Uther won the fight but, with his dying breath, Tristan cursed Camelot to one day suffer his violent and bloody return . . .

That day came courtesy of the sorcerer Nimueh, who raised Sir Tristan from the dead. As a wraith, Tristan took the form of the Black Knight and issued Uther a challenge to single combat.

The challenge was taken up first by Sir Owain and then by Sir Pellinor. Both dealt the Black Knight seemingly fatal blows, but he could not be harmed by any mortal weapon and went on to kill both his opponents. He was prepared to slaughter all who faced him until he could fight the king himself.

FAILED PLANS

Arthur challenged the knight, but at the last moment Uther took his place. The king had realized that his death would stop the phantom. Meanwhile, Merlin discovered there was one very special kind of weapon that could 'kill' a wraith. Armed with a sword burnished by the Great Dragon, Uther once again defeated Sir Tristan in single combat, and the Black Knight exploded into nothing.

VILLAINOUS WORDS

'Single combat. Noon tomorrow. To the death.'

The Black Knight *(Excalibur)*

'Powerful magic can harness the grief and rage of a tormented soul and make it live again.'

Gaius *(Excalibur)*

'You can have what you came for – the father, not the son.'

Uther *(Excalibur)*

DID YOU KNOW?

Sir Tristan's crest was a silver eagle on a black background.

KANAN

THE RAIDER

Merlin has faced those driven to evil acts as a result of terrible suffering, and those who wanted revenge for injustices. He might not always approve of the path they have taken, but he can often understand what led them to it. However, Merlin will never understand people like Kanan, whose sole motivation is greed.

VILLAINY RATING	
Evil intent	★★★
Magical power	
Desire for revenge	★
Sneakiness	★★
Comeuppance	★★★★★

VILLAINOUS DEEDS

Kanan was the leader of a bandit horde. He used violence to take whatever he wanted, no matter what the effect on his victims. When Kanan came to Ealdor, he demanded all the villagers' grain, not caring if they would have enough food left to survive. When Merlin's mother, Hunith, stood up to Kanan, he hit her and killed the villager who came to her aid.

On Kanan's next visit, the villagers were ready for him, helped by Arthur, Merlin, Morgana and Gwen. Kanan fled, but had no intention of staying away for good. Not only was he unwilling to give up Ealdor's grain, but he had been humiliated by Arthur and could not let the prince get the better of him.

FAILED PLANS

Kanan returned when he thought he would have the upper hand. He killed Ealdor's sentry and sent Arthur a warning note stuck to the man's body. Finally, Kanan faced the prince in single combat, and was beaten. He was left for dead but somehow found the strength to try to attack Arthur one last time. Even in his dying moments, Kanan would not concede defeat.

VILLAINOUS WORDS

'Kill them!'

Kanan *(The Moment of Truth)*

'We're going to make Kanan rue the day he ever came to this village.'

Merlin *(The Moment of Truth)*

'Kanan's brutal. He fights only to kill, which is why he'll never defeat us.'

Arthur *(The Moment of Truth)*

DID YOU KNOW?

Kanan had a terrible scar across his face.

TAUREN

VILLAINY RATING	
Evil intent	★★★
Magical power	★★★
Desire for revenge	★★★★
Sneakiness	★★
Comeuppance	★★★★★

FOOL'S GOLD

When the sorcerer Tauren came to Camelot he had with him the Mage Stone, a magical item that had many powers; including the ability to turn lead into gold. But it was not greed that motivated Tauren – it was his desire for revenge on the enemy of all magic-kind. He needed gold to buy his way into Uther's chambers, so he could kill the king . . .

VILLAINOUS DEEDS

Tauren didn't care who got hurt in the process. Gwen's father, Tom, was only one of many who died as a result of associating with this ruthless sorcerer. After he lost the Mage Stone in Tom's forge, Tauren threatened to kill Gwen if she didn't return it to him.

But it was Morgana, not Gwen, who allied herself with the sorcerer. Morgana would lure Uther to her father's grave, where Tauren and his band of rebels would murder him.

FAILED PLANS

Tauren's men were killed by Merlin, but the sorcerer escaped the attack and raced to kill Uther himself. By that time Morgana had realized she didn't want the king dead after all and she betrayed her new ally. As Tauren prepared to stab Uther, Morgana ran him through with the king's sword.

VILLAINOUS WORDS

'The gold was but a means – a means to rid this kingdom of Uther Pendragon once and for all.'

Tauren (*To Kill the King*)

'I want Uther dead. As much as you. As much as anyone in this rotten kingdom of his.'

Morgana to Tauren (*To Kill the King*)

'Die, Uther Pendragon!'

Tauren (*To Kill the King*)

DID YOU KNOW?

Merlin attacked Tauren with Sophia Tirmawr's Sidhe staff, but Tauren repelled its deadly blast with the Mage Stone.

CEDRIC

VILLAINY RATING	
Evil intent	★
Magical power	
Desire for revenge	
Sneakiness	★★★★★
Comeuppance	★★★★★

THE PRINCE'S THIEF

Cedric claimed he came to Camelot to find work, but he was really looking for profit. Cedric was a thief, and when he heard about the tomb full of jewels under the castle, he decided the treasure would be his. He cunningly discovered that the keys to the tomb were held by Prince Arthur. Cedric was so sly that he paid someone for this information – and then stole the pouch of coins back from him!

VILLAINOUS DEEDS

Cedric fawned over the prince and was soon invited on Arthur's hunting trip. During the hunt, Arthur was nearly killed by a boar. Merlin stopped the beast with magic, but Cedric claimed all the credit. When Arthur offered to reward him, Cedric asked for a position in the royal household, where he worked hard to oust Merlin from the post of Arthur's servant.

Having stolen Arthur's keys, Cedric proceeded to ransack the tomb. But when he tried to steal a huge, heart-shaped jewel, he sealed his own fate. The stone contained the soul of an ancient sorcerer – Cornelius Sigan – and the moment Cedric dislodged the jewel, Sigan's soul escaped and took over the thief's body.

FAILED PLANS

Cedric's greed was his downfall. Sigan later abandoned his body, leaving Cedric as a lifeless husk. Cedric may have been a very unpleasant person, but his punishment far outweighed his crime . . .

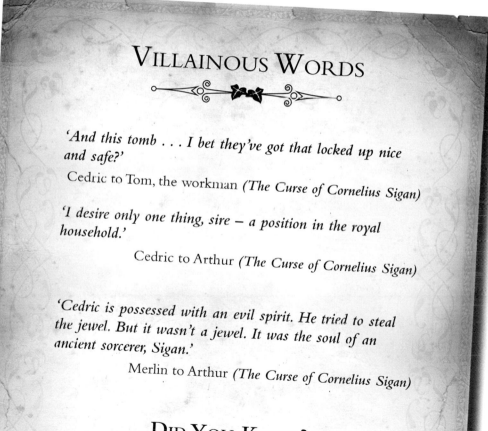

VILLAINOUS WORDS

'And this tomb . . . I bet they've got that locked up nice and safe?'

Cedric to Tom, the workman *(The Curse of Cornelius Sigan)*

'I desire only one thing, sire – a position in the royal household.'

Cedric to Arthur *(The Curse of Cornelius Sigan)*

'Cedric is possessed with an evil spirit. He tried to steal the jewel. But it wasn't a jewel. It was the soul of an ancient sorcerer, Sigan.'

Merlin to Arthur *(The Curse of Cornelius Sigan)*

DID YOU KNOW?

Cedric was an expert 'fingersmith' – a pickpocket.

CORNELIUS SIGAN

THE SORCEROR'S CURSE

Hundreds of years ago, the people of Camelot lived in fear of Cornelius Sigan, the most powerful sorcerer that had ever lived. He could turn day into night and control the tides. Legend had it that his spells even helped to build Camelot itself. But Sigan grew too powerful and the king of the day ordered his execution. Sigan declared that he would one day return to take his revenge, and raze the city to the ground and destroy all its inhabitants.

VILLAINY RATING	
Evil intent	★★★★★
Magical power	★★★★★
Desire for revenge	★★★★★
Sneakiness	★★
Comeuppance	★★

VILLAINOUS DEEDS

As well as wanting revenge, Sigan couldn't bear the thought that his power and wealth would die with him. He became obsessed with finding a way of defeating death and had his soul sealed in a blue, heart-shaped jewel that adorned his sarcophagus. Around the jewel were the runes: 'He who breaks my heart, completes my work.' Sigan knew that one day someone would try to remove the gem; then he would possess their body and live again.

When Cedric the thief broke into Sigan's tomb and removed the stone from the sarcophagus, the sorcerer took over his body and launched his revenge on Camelot. He brought the castle's stone gargoyles to life and sent them to attack the kingdom. Under his command, the palace itself was heavily bombarded and started to collapse.

FAILED PLANS

When Merlin tried to stop Sigan, the sorcerer was impressed by the boy's powers and suggested they join forces. Merlin refused. Sigan left Cedric's body and attempted to take over Merlin's instead, so that he could possess the warlock's magic. Merlin fought him off with a spell from the Great Dragon and trapped his soul back in the heart-shaped jewel. Defeated but not destroyed, Sigan must now wait for another chance to take his revenge on Camelot . . .

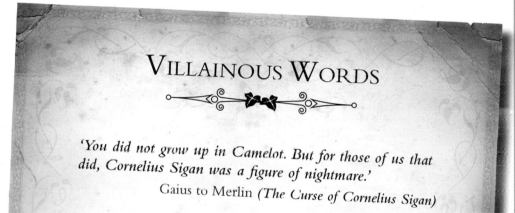

VILLAINOUS WORDS

'You did not grow up in Camelot. But for those of us that did, Cornelius Sigan was a figure of nightmare.'

Gaius to Merlin (*The Curse of Cornelius Sigan*)

'I am returned . . .' Sigan (*The Curse of Cornelius Sigan*)

'Together we can rule over this land. Arthur will tremble at your voice. He will kneel at your feet.'

Sigan to Merlin (*The Curse of Cornelius Sigan*)

DID YOU KNOW?

In the language of the old religion, Sigan means Raven.

ODD MAN OUT

Look carefully at the four lines of villains below.
Can you spot the odd one out in each row?

HOMEWARD BOUND

When Merlin hears that Kanan is laying siege to his home town, he rushes back to try and help his friends and family. Help Merlin through the forest maze to reach his home in time.

START

FINISH

47

KING ODIN

KING OF ASSASSINS

King Odin's son challenged Prince
Arthur to a fight. Arthur had no
quarrel with him and asked him to
withdraw, but the young man wanted
to prove himself and fought on. He
was killed. Odin wanted revenge for
the death of his son – he wanted
Arthur dead.

VILLAINY RATING	
Evil intent	★
Magical power	
Desire for revenge	★★★★★
Sneakiness	★
Comeuppance	★

VILLAINOUS DEEDS

King Odin's desire to see Prince Arthur dead may have been understandable – the grief-stricken king had just lost his son. However, Odin did not act honourably. He summoned Myror, the most feared assassin in all the known lands. This ruthless cut-throat cared nothing for human life, and Odin knew that he would slaughter anyone who stood in his way.

FAILED PLANS

Odin may only have wanted justice for his son, but his actions set in motion a train of events that caused the deaths of several innocent people. Hiring Myror could even have led to war with Camelot – and many more deaths – had Arthur not persuaded Uther to take pity on the grieving father and make peace instead.

VILLAINOUS WORDS

'Are you as ruthless as they say you are? You would kill anyone? You are prepared to kill royalty?'

Odin to Myror *(The Once and Future Queen)*

'I want you to kill the man who murdered my son. I want you to kill Arthur Pendragon.'

Odin to Myror *(The Once and Future Queen)*

'Odin must be made to pay for his actions. We must strike back at him.'

Uther *(The Once and Future Queen)*

DID YOU KNOW?

Odin's crest is a wolf's head.

MYROR

THE SILENT KILLER

The assassin Myror was completely amoral. He saw little difference between killing a human and swatting a fly. He cared only about his fee and keeping his reputation as the most feared assassin in all the known lands.

VILLAINY RATING	
Evil intent	★★★★
Magical power	
Desire for revenge	
Sneakiness	★★★★★
Comeuppance	★★★★★

VILLAINOUS DEEDS

Myror was hired by King Odin to kill Prince Arthur. He proved his suitability by disarming and defeating one of Odin's guards, who drew a sword on him.

Myror's agility and strength were as great as his ruthlessness. He easily climbed the sheer walls of Camelot and later evaded capture by hanging underneath the castle's drawbridge. Although a weapons expert, he favoured the crossbow, which could kill silently from a distance.

FAILED PLANS

As he tried to track down Prince Arthur, Myror thought nothing of killing a guard who got in his way; even Merlin had a narrow escape. When Myror discovered that Arthur was jousting in the tournament, he killed the prince's opponent and took his place, fitting his lance with a retractable blade. Unluckily for Myror, Arthur survived the first blow, and Merlin's magic made Myror's saddle slip. Arthur seized the advantage and unhorsed his opponent. A bad fall meant the assassin would never rise again.

VILLAINOUS WORDS

'I have killed many people. They are all the same to me.'
Myror (The Once and Future Queen)

'I have heard of this Myror . . .'
Uther (The Once and Future Queen)

DID YOU KNOW?

Myror wore hoops in his ears and a fang around his neck.

HENGIST

THE BANDIT KING

Hengist lived the life of a king – a king of bandits. In his run-down castle, piled high with looted goods, he ruled with the threat of violence. Men fought to the death for his amusement or were thrown to his vicious man-eating Wilddeoren.

VILLAINOUS DEEDS

VILLAINY RATING	
Evil intent	★★
Magical power	
Desire for revenge	
Sneakiness	★★★
Comeuppance	★★★★★

On Hengist's orders, the bandit leader Kendrick attempted to kidnap Lady Morgana so Hengist could hold her to ransom. When Hengist discovered that the bandit had instead captured Morgana's servant, Gwen, he threw Kendrick to the Wilddeoren.

FAILED PLANS

Hengist was happy to kill on the slightest whim. When Gwen and her would-be rescuer, Lancelot, came face to face with the Wilddeoren, Hengist watched with enjoyment.

When Arthur and Merlin arrived he simply grabbed a crossbow and prepared to kill them too. But Merlin's magic left Hengist trapped in his own cage, and he met his end in the jaws of his own monsters.

VILLAINOUS WORDS

'If Hengist is holding her, it would take a small army to rescue your maid.'
Uther to Morgana (*Lancelot and Guinevere*)

'Release the Wilddeoren!'
Hengist (*Lancelot and Guinevere*)

DID YOU KNOW?
Hengist came from the kingdom of Mercia.

LADY CATRINA

VILLAINY RATING	
Evil intent	★★★
Magical power	★★★★
Desire for revenge	★★★★★
Sneakiness	★★★★★
Comeuppance	★★★★★

THE UGLY TRUTH

Lady Catrina of the House of Tregor was a welcome visitor in Camelot, and Uther soon found himself deeply attracted to the beautiful, genteel noblewoman. But Catrina's appearance was very deceptive. In reality she was a troll – foul-smelling, bad-mannered and totally desperate for wealth and power.

VILLAINOUS DEEDS

Gaius' suspicions were aroused by Lady Catrina's apparent recovery from the incurable bone disease for which he'd treated her as a child, and investigations by Merlin uncovered her true identity. Uther refused to listen to Gaius' warnings, and once Catrina had given a magical pendant to the king, she made sure that he was completely under her spell. Uther announced that he and Catrina were to be married the next day.

Merlin cast the Spell of Revelation to show Catrina's true appearance to the king, but she was able to resist it.

Despite Merlin's best efforts, the wedding went ahead. Catrina accused Merlin of stealing her family seal, and Uther ordered the boy's arrest. Meanwhile, the troll was working to undermine Prince Arthur, and persuaded the king to make her the heir to the throne.

FAILED PLANS

Although Merlin managed to switch Catrina's transformation potion with a fake one made by Gaius, Uther was too bewitched to notice that his beautiful bride had become an ugly troll. The Great Dragon informed Merlin that the only way to break the enchantment was for Uther to cry tears of real regret. Finally Catrina's deception was revealed, but she fought off all Uther's guards and only Merlin's magic enabled Arthur to defeat the troll.

VILLAINOUS WORDS

'Camelot and all its riches will soon be mine.'

Lady Catrina *(Beauty and the Beast)*

'Your scent, it's so fragrant.'

'Well, it's mostly dung.'

Uther and Catrina *(Beauty and the Beast)*

DID YOU KNOW?

Gaius' fake potion for Catrina consisted of rat guts, toad paste, horse dung, one sheep's eyeball, pond scum, three wolf spiders and a dash of sheep's brain.

JONAS

THE TROLL'S SERVANT

When the alleged Lady Catrina – a troll in disguise – came to Camelot, she brought with her her strange, non-human servant Jonas. Jonas might have only been obeying orders, but he enjoyed thwarting Merlin at every step, revelled in using violence and was eager for Catrina to rule Camelot.

VILLAINOUS DEEDS

When Jonas learned that Merlin was magical and might threaten their plans, he pretended to be the troll's prisoner, tricking Merlin into going to Catrina's lair alone. Although Merlin escaped from the trap, Jonas was waiting for him. He used his incredible strength to keep the warlock from interrupting Uther and Catrina's wedding ceremony, and eagerly helped Catrina in her endeavours to become heir to the throne.

VILLAINY RATING	
Evil intent	★★★
Magical power	★★★★
Desire for revenge	
Sneakiness	★★★★
Comeuppance	★★★★★

FAILED PLANS

After Catrina's true identity was discovered, Jonas tried to stab Arthur, who had been knocked out. But the prince recovered in the nick of time, and Jonas met his end by Arthur's sword.

VILLAINOUS WORDS

'You look positively foul.'

Jonas to Catrina (*Beauty and the Beast*)

'Think of all the money and the power. Soon it will all be yours.'

Jonas to Catrina (*Beauty and the Beast*)

DID YOU KNOW?

Jonas has a tail!

AREDIAN

THE WITCHFINDER

Aredian worked with Uther in the days of the Great Purge. He made his money hunting down suspected sorcerers and interrogating them. Everyone he captured was burned at the stake; many of those killed were friends of Gaius. Since then, Aredian has been in pursuit of sorcery – all the while making a tidy profit for himself.

VILLAINOUS DEEDS

When the result of one of Merlin's spells was observed by a villager, Uther summoned Aredian and offered to pay him any price to find the sorcerer. The Witchfinder suspected Merlin, but it was Gaius who was arrested when a magical amulet was found in his chambers. Aredian persuaded Uther to let him use any methods necessary to obtain a confession from the physician.

VILLAINY RATING	
Evil intent	★★★★
Magical power	
Desire for revenge	★
Sneakiness	★★★★★
Comeuppance	★★★★★

Aredian's cruelty marked him out as a villain from the start. His actions might have been more understandable if he had been truly devoted to his cause but he was simply corrupt and greedy. The Witchfinder claimed to hate magic, but he was really only after the gold he got for discovering a sorcerer. Aredian manipulated witnesses, planted the amulet in Gaius' chambers and used trickery to bring about the deaths of many innocent people.

FAILED PLANS

The Witchfinder came to a sticky end when Merlin turned the tables and framed him as a sorcerer. Aredian tried to take Morgana hostage in order to escape, but Merlin's spell caused him to fall to his death from a castle window.

VILLAINOUS WORDS

'The Witchfinder serves no one. He is a law unto himself.'
Uther (The Witchfinder)

'You have grown lazy, Uther. You have grown idle. Your once noble Camelot is rotten to the core . . . You stand on the brink of dark oblivion.'
Aredian (The Witchfinder)

'His powers are uncanny. Once he has the scent of magic, nothing can stop him.'
Gaius (The Witchfinder)

'Believe me, Gaius, by the time I've finished with you, you'll beg to confess.'
Aredian (The Witchfinder)

DID YOU KNOW?

Aredian used eye drops containing belladonna to give visions of magic to his 'witnesses'.

KENDRICK

THE OUTLAW

On the orders of bandit king Hengist, Kendrick and his men ambushed Lady Morgana's party in the woods. Her entourage was killed, and Morgana and Gwen were captured.

VILLAINOUS DEEDS

While Morgana distracted Kendrick, Gwen stole his sword. The girls escaped, but he gave chase and recaptured Gwen. Unfortunately, it was Morgana Hengist wanted. Kendrick demanded that Gwen masquerade as her mistress so that he wouldn't have to return empty-handed to Hengist.

FAILED PLANS

The ruse worked – for a while. But when Hengist grew suspicious over the lack of contact between Uther and the supposed 'Morgana', he threatened Kendrick until the bandit admitted the truth. Furious at the deception, Hengist threw Kendrick to the man-eating Wilddoreon.

VILLAINOUS WORDS

'I have no intention of harming you – at least not yet. You're much more valuable to me alive, Lady Morgana.'

Kendrick *(Lancelot and Guinevere)*

'I will not impersonate my mistress.'
'Then you will die where you stand.'

Gwen and Kendrick *(Lancelot and Guinevere)*

DID YOU KNOW?

The name Kendrick is of Welsh origin and means 'greatest champion.'

HALIG

VILLAINY RATING

VILLAINY RATING	
Evil intent	★★★
Magical power	
Desire for revenge	
Sneakiness	★★
Comeuppance	★★★★★

THE BOUNTY HUNTER

Halig was a cruel man who captured magical beings and handed them over to Uther in return for payment. Those who agreed with Uther's view on sorcery might have seen him as a hero, but Halig was only motivated by greed. He took pleasure in his unsavoury job, with no thought for those who faced death as a result of his actions.

VILLAINOUS DEEDS

Halig proved himself to be ruthless and violent in his search for the Druid girl Freya, who escaped him. When he suspected Merlin of harbouring her, he was about to beat a confession out of the young warlock until Arthur intervened.

FAILED PLANS

Going after the Druid girl turned out to be a very bad move for Halig. Freya was a Bastet – a cursed creature – and she killed Halig when he tried to recapture her.

VILLAINOUS WORDS

'Merlin, bounty hunters are vicious men; they are not to be messed with. You of all people should understand that.'

Gaius (*The Lady of the Lake*)

DID YOU KNOW?

Halig was tipped off about Freya by one of her fellow Druids, which was highly unusual. This should have been a warning to Halig of how very dangerous the girl might be!

KING ALINED

VILLAINY RATING

VILLAINY RATING	
Evil intent	★★★
Magical power	
Desire for revenge	
Sneakiness	★★★★
Comeuppance	★

THIRSTY FOR WAR

King Alined's cowardice and greed
threatened the lives of hundreds –
possibly thousands – of innocent
people. War had proved profitable
for Alined, so he did all he could
to sabotage Uther's peace talks
with his rival leaders, including
King Olaf. If Alined's plan
had succeeded, the five
kingdoms would
have been
plunged back
into war.

VILLAINOUS DEEDS

Alined instructed his jester Trickler, a sorcerer, to make Arthur and King Olaf's daughter, Vivian, fall in love with each other. This threatened to bring Olaf's wrath down on Camelot, because while Olaf was a just and fair leader, he had a ferocious temper when it came to protecting his precious daughter.

FAILED PLANS

Merlin and Gaius managed to thwart Alined's plan, but the selfish king escaped any punishment for his warmongering. Merlin decided to keep Alined's secret, fearing that if Uther knew about the use of magic on his son, then a fresh war would have broken out – giving Alined precisely what he wanted in the first place.

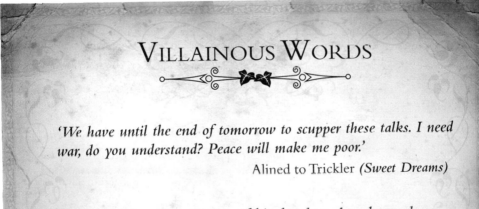

VILLAINOUS WORDS

'We have until the end of tomorrow to scupper these talks. I need war, do you understand? Peace will make me poor.'

Alined to Trickler *(Sweet Dreams)*

'Olaf is supremely protective of his daughter. An advance by Arthur would be a sure-fire way to ruin the peace talks.'

Gaius to Merlin *(Sweet Dreams)*

DID YOU KNOW?

Alined's territory does not directly border Camelot, but peace with his kingdom is vitally important for the prosperity of Uther and his people.

TRICKLER

THE KING'S JESTER

Trickler, jester to King Alined, used sorcery to carry out his master's wishes. Alined wanted to cause conflict between King Uther and King Olaf, so he had Trickler use magic to make Prince Arthur fall in love with Olaf's daughter, Vivian.

Although Trickler was only obeying orders, he enjoyed creating chaos. When Alined's plans failed, however, the jester suffered his king's wrath.

VILLAINY RATING	
Evil intent	★★
Magical power	★★★
Desire for revenge	
Sneakiness	★★★★
Comeuppance	★

Villainous Words

'Enough. There will be time for snivelling when the axe is over your head. Now there is work to be done.'

Alined to Trickler *(Sweet Dreams)*

'But the enchantment is strong, my lord. Sooner or later the two will be drawn together.' Trickler to Alined *(Sweet Dreams)*

Did You Know?

Trickler got away with breathing fire and conjuring butterflies in front of Uther because his magic looked more like the 'magic tricks' of an entertainer than the spells of a sorcerer.

RACE FOR THE CRYSTAL

Alvarr is desperately looking for the Crystal of Neahtid. Which path will lead him to it?

A

C

B

WHAT'S IN A NAME?

Can you work out what missing letters will complete the words on the left and right to reveal the name of a villainous court jester?

B	O	A		R	O	L	L	
	S	T	A		A	G	E	
	M	I	N		D	O	L	
M	U	S	I		H	O	I	R
B	L	A	C		N	I	G	H	T
	L	U	L		O	S	E	
	L	I	V		V	I	L	
		O	A		A	N		

The name is _ _ _ _ _ _ _ _

ALVARR

THE RENEGADE

When Alvarr was a child, his parents were killed during the Great Purge. Orphaned, he went into hiding – just like Mordred. Or at least this was the story Alvarr told Morgana when he needed her sympathy; if true, it would certainly explain his hatred of Uther.

VILLAINOUS DEEDS

Alvarr came to Camelot to steal a precious relic of the old religion – the Crystal of Neahtid. Many have lost their lives trying to reclaim it but Alvarr succeeded due to his outward charm, and shocking capacity for dishonesty and violence.

Alvarr knew that the crystal could bestow secrets of the past, the present and the future. He hoped that Mordred would be able to harness this power and use it as a devastating weapon.

Alvarr needed an ally in the royal household to help him steal the crystal, and he chose Morgana. He used her affection for Mordred to gain her trust, and took advantage of her fear and loneliness.

Morgana was horrified to learn that Alvarr planned to strike down not only Uther but all those who served him. The warlock wore down her scruples, convincing her that this was war and sacrifices were necessary. Exploiting Morgana's frustration with Uther and her deep need for acceptance, Alvarr told her she was being brave and heroic.

FAILED PLANS

Alvarr was captured by Arthur, and sentenced to death for treason, but Morgana once more betrayed her king to help him escape. Alvarr might have lost the crystal but he has gained a powerful ally in Morgana, and lives to challenge Uther another day . . .

VILLAINOUS WORDS

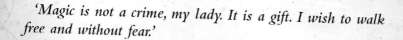

'*Magic is not a crime, my lady. It is a gift. I wish to walk free and without fear.*'

Alvarr to Morgana *(The Witch's Quickening)*

'*He is a fanatic. His supporters follow him unthinkingly, blinded by his charisma.*' Gaius *(The Witch's Quickening)*

'*It is my hope that, with time, Mordred will master the crystal. And when he does we will strike Uther down. Uther and all who serve him.*'

Alvarr to Morgana *(The Witch's Quickening)*

DID YOU KNOW?

Alvarr has Morgana utterly under his spell without any need for sorcery, but unknown to the king's ward, Alvarr already has a consort – Enmyria, one of his followers.

MORDRED

FIRST IMPRESSIONS

The Druid boy Mordred seemed harmless when Merlin first met him; though it was obvious he had magic. Under threat from Uther while in Camelot, Mordred found asylum in Morgana's company, and was later safely returned to his people by Prince Arthur. Although Mordred showed no outward signs of villainy, the Great Dragon told Merlin that if the child lived, he would one day kill Arthur.

VILLAINOUS DEEDS

Merlin met Mordred again in the Forest of Ascetir. He witnessed the strength of the boy's magic when his scream felled three guards in a violent but desperate act of self defence. Though dangerous, Mordred did not demonstrate a desire to harm or kill others.

VILLAINY RATING	
Evil intent	★★★
Magical power	★★★★★
Desire for revenge	★★
Sneakiness	★ ★
Comeuppance	

Later, it was Mordred who convinced Morgana to ally herself with the rebel Alvarr and steal the Crystal of Neahtid. Alvarr hoped Mordred could use the crystal as a weapon to overthrow Uther.

FAILED PLANS

Alvarr's plan failed and his renegade camp was raided by Arthur and his men. This time, Mordred showed no compunction in killing the guards. What Merlin witnessed was no act of self defence, but a deliberate attack. Mordred knew that his near-capture was Merlin's fault and he vowed never to forget this betrayal.

LOOK TO THE FUTURE

Mordred's dark side seems to be growing. Could the Druid boy one day become the ultimate villain and a real threat to the once and future king?

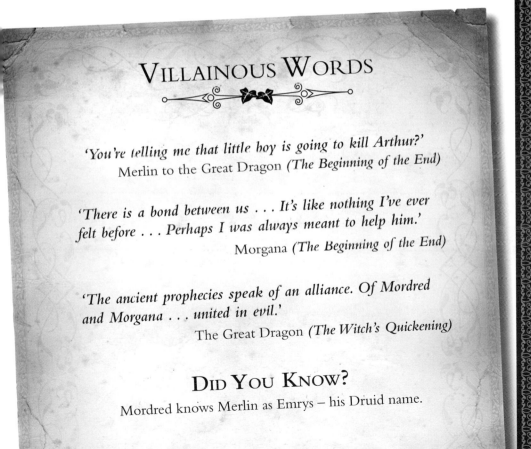

VILLAINOUS WORDS

'You're telling me that little boy is going to kill Arthur?'
Merlin to the Great Dragon (*The Beginning of the End*)

'There is a bond between us . . . It's like nothing I've ever felt before . . . Perhaps I was always meant to help him.'
Morgana (*The Beginning of the End*)

'The ancient prophecies speak of an alliance. Of Mordred and Morgana . . . united in evil.'
The Great Dragon (*The Witch's Quickening*)

DID YOU KNOW?

Mordred knows Merlin as Emrys – his Druid name.

MORGAUSE

A BLOODY RETURN

Morgause, Morgana's older half-sister, was widely believed to have died at birth. But in truth she was smuggled out of Camelot by Gaius and put safely into the care of the high priestesses of the old religion. She returned to Camelot as an adult to end Uther's reign and right his many wrongs – and to meet her sister for the first time.

VILLAINY RATING	
Evil intent	★★★★
Magical power	★★★★★
Desire for revenge	★★★★★
Sneakiness	★★★★
Comeuppance	★

VILLAINOUS DEEDS

Morgause's return to Camelot was blood-splattered – she fought her way into the citadel with a sword, killing five of Uther's men. Disguised in armour, she then challenged Arthur to a duel – a duel which she went on to win. Morgause was revealed to be an enchantress, and she used her magic to bring Arthur's mother, Ygraine, back from the dead. Her motive was not kindly: she hoped to sow discord between father and son, and she succeeded. Stunned to learn the truth about his birth, Arthur returned to Camelot in a rage and challenged Uther to a fight to the death. Much to Morgause's fury, Merlin managed to put an end to the battle and restore peace between Arthur and Uther.

VILLAINOUS DEEDS

Thwarted, Morgause wrought a new plan. Using Morgana as a familiar, she cast a powerful spell to send everyone in Camelot to sleep. With the citadel utterly defenceless, she resurrected the deadly Knights of Medhir and, riding at their helm, led them to the sleeping city in order to kill Uther.

Although ruthless, Morgause does care for her half-sister. When Merlin poisoned Morgana to end the sleeping spell, Morgause quickly struck a deal with him – putting her sister's life before her desire for revenge.

FAILED PLANS

Morgause escaped Camelot by magic, taking Morgana with her. Neither sister has been seen since, but it's hard to believe that Morgause will give up her quest to see Uther vanquished . . .

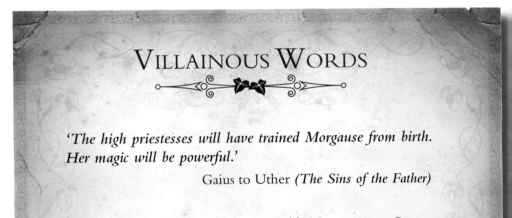

VILLAINOUS WORDS

'The high priestesses will have trained Morgause from birth. Her magic will be powerful.'

Gaius to Uther *(The Sins of the Father)*

'Have you ever imagined a new world, Morgana . . . One where Uther was no more?'

Morgause *(The Witch's Quickening)*

DID YOU KNOW?

Morgause gave Morgana a bracelet that was handed down to her by her mother. It was this bracelet that helped Gaius identify Morgause, as it once belonged to the House of Gorlois – Morgana's family.

Knights of Medhir

Deathly Knights

Three centuries before Uther's reign, seven noble knights were seduced by a sorcerer and became a terrible force that swept through the land, bringing death and destruction. When the sorcerer was defeated, the knights became statues in the Fortress of Idirsholas, and there they stayed silent and still until they were revived by Morgause.

VILLAINY RATING	
Evil intent	★★★★
Magical power	★★★
Desire for revenge	
Sneakiness	
Comeuppance	

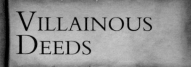

VILLAINOUS DEEDS

When Arthur investigated the fortress, his men were slaughtered by the Knights of Medhir. It was only Merlin's magic and quick thinking that saved Arthur. The knights then moved on to a defenceless Camelot, where Morgause had put every last person into an enchanted sleep.

FAILED PLANS

Morgause's goal was to kill the king, and with the help of her ancient knights she almost succeeded. But Merlin and Arthur had escaped the sleeping spell, and Merlin managed to force Morgause to undo her magic by threatening Morgana's life. As soon as Morgause surrendered, the Knights of Medhir became lifeless once more.

VILLAINOUS WORDS

'When the fires of Idirsholas burn, the Knights of Medhir will ride again.'
Gaius

DID YOU KNOW?

The Knights of Medhir have no power or free will of their own, but once awoken by a sorcerer they are capable of fighting on relentlessly – deadly, invulnerable and immortal.

UTHER

VILLAINY RATING	
Evil intent	★
Magical power	
Desire for revenge	★★★★★
Sneakiness	
Comeuppance	★★

AN UNUSUAL VILLAIN

Although not a villain in
the conventional sense,
many would argue that
Uther's actions cast him
in such a light. He always
tries to act in a way he
believes is best for his
people, but this has often
led to tragic and violent
consequences.

VILLAINOUS DEEDS

When magic helped him produce a son, Uther was thrilled. But when the old religion restored balance to the world, taking a life for a life, and his wife Ygraine died, Uther set out to purge the kingdom of all those who practised magic or followed the old religion. Many people died – and continue to die.

Uther would insist that magic is evil and that he has acted to protect his subjects. But it could also be argued that Uther's brutal war is simply an act of revenge for Ygraine's death. And how does that make Uther any different from Edwin Muir, Nimueh, Morgause, or Alvarr, all of whom also acted to avenge the deaths of loved ones?

The Greater Good

What cannot be disputed is that Uther is a believer in the greater good. He makes sacrifices he thinks will benefit the kingdom. When famine struck he rationed food, giving his knights the greater share, knowing that some of his subjects might starve as a result. He reasoned that if Camelot were unprotected then the kingdom and its people would be vulnerable to attack from vicious outsiders, therefore suffering a worse fate.

Failed Plans

Although none of Uther's actions are driven by openly villainous intent, his hostility towards magic and his often hard-hearted decisions have caused great suffering for his people.

Villainous Words

'Arthur, one day you will be king, then you will understand that these decisions must be made. There are dark forces that threaten this kingdom . . .'

Uther (*The Mark of Nimueh*)

'You have blood on your hands, Uther Pendragon. Blood that will never wash away! A king is meant to be wise and just. You are neither. You rule only with the sword.'

Morgana to Uther (*To Kill the King*)

Did You Know?

Uther did not inherit the throne, but made himself king by conquering all his opponents.

THE GREAT DRAGON

AN ANCIENT BEAST

The Great Dragon, Kilgharrah, is an ancient, magnificent and magical creature of the old religion. Before Uther's time, he and his kind lived wild, supremely powerful and respected by all. But when Uther declared war on all magical beings, he used the Dragonlords to kill every last one. All except Kilgharrah, whom he kept imprisoned as a symbol of his triumph over magic. The Great Dragon was chained up for over twenty years, full of rage and desperate to be free.

VILLAINY RATING	
Evil intent	★★
Magical power	★★★★★
Desire for revenge	★★★★★
Sneakiness	★★★★★
Comeuppance	★★★

Kilgharrah helped Merlin do good, but only when it served his personal desire to be released. The Dragon used his knowledge and cunning to bargain with Merlin. He saved Camelot from the sorcerer Sigan on the condition that Merlin set him free, and he later shared his knowledge about the Crystal of Neahtid to force Merlin to fulfil this promise.

VILLAINOUS DEEDS

Once released, the Dragon caused great harm. Thanks to Uther he was the last of his kind and magic had all but disappeared from the land. Kilgharrah's anger made him seek revenge, and his grief drove him to lash out senselessly to get at Uther. He laid siege to Camelot, burning the citadel and attacking its citizens, including Arthur and Merlin.

FAILED PLANS

Finally, Merlin spoke to Kilgharrah in the dragon-tongue inherited from his father and the Dragon was rendered helpless. Merlin chose to show mercy on the beast; ordering the creature to leave Camelot and never return. The Great Dragon stood humbled. He departed with the promise that he would not forget Merlin's clemency.

A Complicated Creature

The Great Dragon is a complicated creature, not easily labelled either a villain or a hero. He is cunning, certainly, and always acts to serve his own needs and the interests of the old religion. But after more than twenty years of brutal treatment, can he truly be condemned for his selfish and savage behaviour?

VILLAINOUS WORDS

'Only if Uther dies can magic return to the land.
Only if Uther dies will you be free, Merlin.
Uther's reign is at an end. Let Arthur's reign
begin . . . fulfil your destiny . . .'

The Great Dragon *(To Kill the King)*

'You have failed in your destiny, young warlock. Arthur
is all but dead — and you will soon be joining him.'
The Great Dragon *(The Last Dragonlord)*

DID YOU KNOW?
A Dragon's heart is on its right side, not its left.

ANSWERS

Page 8

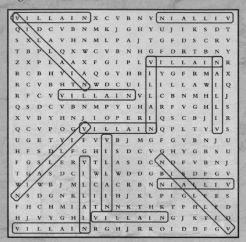

Page 9

1. KANAN
2. TAUREN
3. SIGAN
4. MORGAUSE
5. NIMUEH

Page 20

Page 21

Knight Valiant travelled from the Western Isles.

Page 28

There are 42 beetles

Page 29

VENGEANCE

Page 30

To save myself from a mortal death i must offer another mortal soul in sacrifice

Page 31

Sophia and Aulfric were Sidhe.

Page 46

Page 47

Page 70

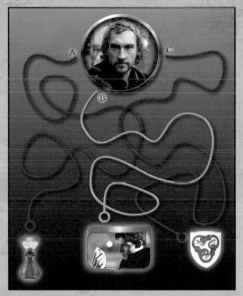

Page 71
The villainous court jester was Trickler.

THE ADVENTURES OF MERLIN: EPISODE GUIDE

Series 1

Episode 1 – *The Dragon's Call*

Episode 2 – *Valiant*

Episode 3 – *The Mark of Nimueh*

Episode 4 – *The Poisoned Chalice*

Episode 5 – *Lancelot*

Episode 6 – *A Remedy to Cure All Ills*

Episode 7 – *The Gates of Avalon*

Episode 8 – *The Beginning of the End*

Episode 9 – *Excalibur*

Episode 10 – *The Moment of Truth*

Episode 11 – *The Labyrinth of Gedref*

Episode 12 – *To Kill the King*

Episode 13 – *Le Morte D'Arthur*

Series 2

INDEX

94

MORE EXCITING MERLIN BOOKS!

THE MAGIC BEGINS

POTIONS AND POISON

SWORD AND SORCERY

A FIGHTING CHANCE

DANGEROUS QUESTS

MERLIN
The Dragon's Call

MERLIN
Valiant

MERLIN
The Mark of Nimueh

MERLIN
The Poisoned Chalice

MERLIN
The Death of Arthur

MERLIN
The Labyrinth of Gedref

MYSTERY ACTIVITY BOOK

QUEST ACTIVITY BOOK

POTIONS & SPELLS
ACTIVITY BOOK

THE COMPLETE GUIDE